HOW TO USE THIS BOOK

This exciting, interactive adventure story features questions throughout. When you reach a question, stop! To unlock the next part of the story, you must find the right answer. DON'T SKIP AHEAD until you've worked it out! Check that your solution is correct by turning to the answers at the back of the book.

Watch for the DATA BLAST pages throughout. These are packed with science facts and explanations. Read them carefully, because they will help you answer the questions. If you don't know the answer to a question, turn back to the previous Data Blast page.

SAFETY WARNING

The stories in this book use exciting situations to illustrate important scientific principles. They are NOT intended as suggestions of activities for you to try at home. You should NOT attempt to make your own parachute, explore inside a live volcano, or roll a truck over a cliff edge.

Molly Cool, Andy Matter, and Tess Tube volunteer at the Metro City Science Museum. One day, they spot a shattered glass cabinet.

"Something's been stolen!" cries Molly.

Molly

Tess

Andy

"Wait, there's a note," says Tess Tube.
"It's from the thief!"

Greetings FOOLS,

That's right! I have STOLEN your reversium, and KIDNAPPED the museum's curator! Ha, ha, ha. Reversium, as you know, is the only material that can make time go backward. Such a rare and interesting material deserves to be in the hands of a REAL scientist, not a bunch of AMATEURS. I have taken it to my secret laboratory on ATOMIC ISLAND. I will use it to hold the whole world to ransom!

Yours,

Dr. Adam Smasher

"We have stop Dr. Smasher!" says Molly.

"Wait," says Tess. "The burglar also seems to have dropped some pages from a science book. Perhaps they contain information that will help us?"

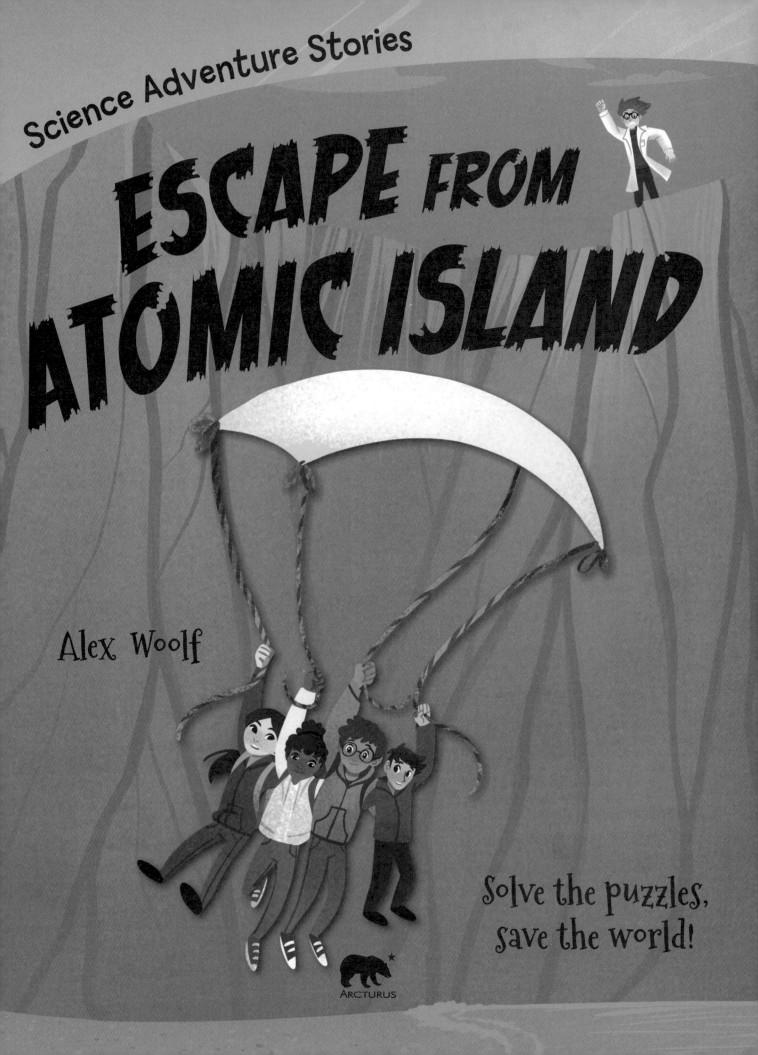

ARCTURUS

This edition published in 2020 by Arcturus Publishing Limited
26/27 Bickels Yard, 151–153 Bermondsey Street,
London SE1 3HA

Author: Alex Woolf
Illustrator: Geraldine Rodriguez
Editors: Rachel Cooke, Polly Goodman, and Joe Harris
Designers: Stefan Holliland and Emma Randall

ISBN: 978-1-83940-318-7
CH008101NT
Supplier 33, Date 0220, Print run 9662

Printed in China

What is STEM?

STEM is a world-wide initiative
that aims to cultivate an
interest in Science, Technology,
Engineering, and Mathematics,
in an effort to promote these
disciplines to as wide a variety of
students as possible.

DATA BLAST

Check it out!

STEEL and TUNGSTEN are hard metals.

LEAD and COPPER are soft and easy to shape.

MATERIALS with different properties are useful for different tasks. Sometimes you might want a strong material—such as steel. Sometimes you might need something air can pass through—such as cloth. Sometimes you might want something that does not melt easily—such as tungsten, which has a high melting point.

SILVER and GLASS are reflective.

GLASS and TUNGSTEN shatter easily.

When materials change, their properties change, too. Some changes can be reversed—for example, water can be frozen, and ice can be melted. Others are irreversible.

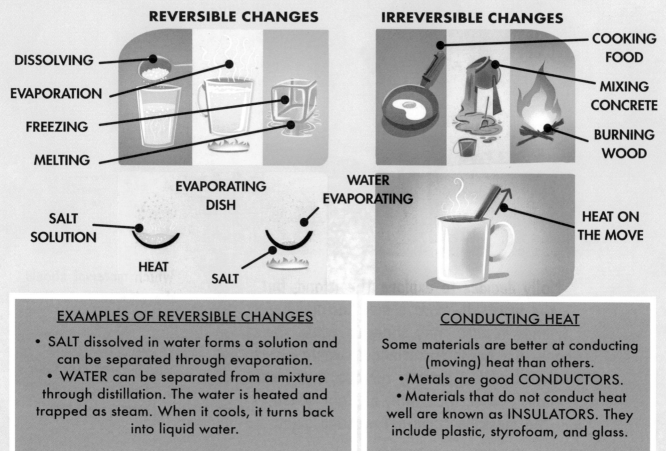

REVERSIBLE CHANGES

- DISSOLVING
- EVAPORATION
- FREEZING
- MELTING

IRREVERSIBLE CHANGES

- COOKING FOOD
- MIXING CONCRETE
- BURNING WOOD

EVAPORATING DISH

SALT SOLUTION

HEAT

WATER EVAPORATING

SALT

HEAT ON THE MOVE

EXAMPLES OF REVERSIBLE CHANGES

- SALT dissolved in water forms a solution and can be separated through evaporation.
- WATER can be separated from a mixture through distillation. The water is heated and trapped as steam. When it cools, it turns back into liquid water.

CONDUCTING HEAT

Some materials are better at conducting (moving) heat than others.
- Metals are good CONDUCTORS.
- Materials that do not conduct heat well are known as INSULATORS. They include plastic, styrofoam, and glass.

5

Molly, Andy, and Tess set out on a boat for Atomic Island. But on the way, the boat gets tossed around on giant waves. Molly falls overboard! Hours later, she wakes up on a beach alone. She is surrounded by wreckage—is it from the boat?

This rock is sharp. Could I use it to write?

Molly decides to explore the island, but she wants to leave a message for her friends in case they show up while she's gone. She needs something to write on—a material with a smooth surface that's soft enough to scratch into, but not so soft the message could get washed away.

Which material should she choose to write a message on?

(a) Beach sand
(b) Copper saucepan
(d) Steel panel
(e) Plastic bottle

Near the beach, Molly finds a metal door that has rusted shut. She returns to the beach to find something that will help her open it. She's overjoyed to find her friends waiting for her there.

I found a lead pipe, wooden poles, and a tungsten bowl.

Great beachcombing!

I've got a steel rod, styrofoam, cloths, and a roll of silver foil.

Tess and Andy show Molly a collection of objects they've managed to retrieve from the wreckage of their boat. "Tungsten is the hardest metal," says Andy. "If we bash that door with the tungsten bowl, might it open?"

What might go wrong with tungsten? What could they use as an alternative?

The door from the beach leads into a live volcano! It's incredibly hot. They hear Dr. Smasher's voice over a loudspeaker. "Welcome to Atomic Island—the hottest place to be. I hope you like it here ... since you can never leave!"

You kids will rue the day you decided to meddle in MY plans!

It's hard to breathe!

I don't lava this!

The door back to the beach makes a click. "It's locked!" says Andy. The lava bubbles and smokes dangerously beneath them. It releases gases that make them choke.

What material can they use to protect themselves from fumes, while still being able to breathe?
(a) The tungsten bowl
(b) Silver foil
(c) Cloth

Molly, Adam, and Tess make themselves masks. Together they explore the volcano's interior, searching for an escape. They find the start of a tunnel, but it's blocked by a pair of steel doors.

Let's melt the doors with lava.

But how do we carry the lava here?

Scorching idea, Tess!

They search for an object they can use to transport the super-hot lava to the doors. It needs to be made of a material with a very high melting point.

COPPER

SILVER

TUNGSTEN

WOOD

STYROFOAM

Which of these objects should they use?

Molly, Andy, and Tess venture closer to the pool of lava. It is extremely hot and they start to sweat. Suddenly, the ground shakes and a huge, red-hot fountain shoots into the air, landing close to their feet. They stagger backward in shock.

Once they've recovered, the trio continue toward the lava. Molly kneels down, preparing to scoop up some of the lava.

Wait! Is metal a conductor or insulator of heat?

That's the burning question.

Is metal a conductor or insulator of heat?

"If it's a conductor, then the heat will move from the lava through the metal to my hand," says Molly. "I could get burnt—unless I can find an insulator to put between the metal and my skin."

What material could Tess use as an insulator?

They melt the steel doors and break through to the tunnel beyond. After a short walk, they emerge by a lagoon. Beside it is a train track with a steam train on it. Standing on top is a ten-year-old boy!

It's me, Mike Slater, the museum curator!

Didn't you have a beard?

I thought your hair was white!

"Adam Smasher used the reversium to reverse time, and turn me into a kid!" says Mike. "I escaped from his laboratory in this train. I could take you back, but it's run out of fresh water for the boiler. The water in the lagoon is salty."

How can they make fresh water from the saltwater lagoon? The correct answer is hidden in this wordsearch. Also, look for the words "saltwater," "lagoon," and "separate."

X	U	O	E	O	G	X	G	D	N	R	A
A	A	P	A	X	L	U	R	I	U	M	S
R	P	S	S	R	R	N	G	S	K	S	K
G	A	D	T	E	X	I	O	T	G	E	E
P	S	P	U	T	P	P	S	I	A	G	O
O	E	R	E	A	D	A	X	L	D	C	O
A	R	E	D	W	R	S	R	L	E	X	R
G	P	G	A	T	E	E	E	A	Z	E	R
E	O	G	N	L	D	D	I	T	T	O	E
G	G	L	I	A	E	D	R	I	R	E	P
E	R	S	G	S	O	O	R	O	E	R	S
S	E	O	L	A	G	O	O	N	O	E	A

Molly, Andy, and Tess make fresh water, which they pour into the locomotive's boiler. Mike lights a fire, which heats the water to create steam. The steam builds up pressure in the engine, which drives the locomotive. Soon, they are puffing along the track.

And then, quite suddenly, it starts snowing!

A huge voice booms out from the mountain. "I know you've hijacked my train!" bellows Dr. Smasher. "However, thanks to my stolen reversium, I can rewind the weather to last winter … and freeze the tracks!"

The train can't travel any further on these icy tracks.

We need to make salt to melt the ice.

Remember, the lagoon's water is salty.

What method can they use to extract the salt from the saltwater? Work it out from this anagram: "AVIATOR OPEN."

The train chugs past a half-built railway station and stops in a tunnel. Mike points to a doorway ahead. "There's Smasher's underground lab," he says.

From behind them comes the sound of another approaching train. Dr. Smasher and his guards are coming after them!

Molly runs back to the half-built station. She picks up a bag of cement. "We can make concrete with this and pour it over the tracks," she says.

They mix the cement with water to make concrete and pour it over the tracks. "Hold on!" says Andy. "Can't Smasher just melt the concrete and turn it back into cement and water?"

Can concrete be turned back into cement and water?

After blocking up the tunnel, they enter Smasher's laboratory. It's freezing cold in there. They soon see why ... "Smasher's encased the reversium in a block of ice!" says Molly.

"Let's smash it to ice cubes," says Andy, attacking it with a hammer.

"It's too big," says Tess. "It'll take too long. We need to think of something else."

Then Molly has a spark of inspiration. "We could build a fire," she suggests.

What will happen if they heat it? Will it burn or melt? Will it turn into water or steam?

DATA BLAST

"The hot topic," says Tess, "is how do you build a fire? Let's find out."

THE FIRE TRIANGLE: OXYGEN + FUEL (MATERIAL CONTAINING CARBON) + HEAT = FIRE

OXYGEN

HEAT

FUEL

Some materials, such as wood, burn because they contain the element carbon. When they are heated to a certain temperature, the carbon inside them reacts with oxygen in the air and they burst into flames. This is called their "combustion point." Because their combustion point is lower than their melting point, they burn rather than melt. All living matter, or matter that was once living, contains carbon.

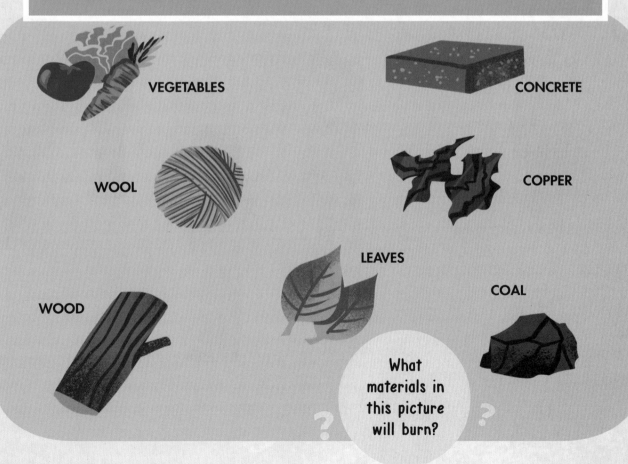

VEGETABLES

CONCRETE

WOOL

COPPER

LEAVES

COAL

WOOD

What materials in this picture will burn?

15

Soon they've gathered lots of material in a big pile. They have their fuel. They have oxygen (in the air). Now all they need is heat to make a fire. Mike takes out a box of matches and prepares to set light to the pile.

"Wait!" says Molly. "We need to plan what we're going to do once the ice melts. How are we going to get the heavy block of reversium out of this underground lab and back home?"

"Let's see if there are any clues here," says Tess, taking out the torn pages they found in the museum.

Check it out!

DATA BLAST

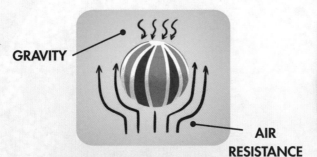

GRAVITY

AIR RESISTANCE

AIR PUMPED IN

FLOATING AND SINKING
If the density of an object is equal to or less than the density of the water it displaces (pushes aside), then the object will float. For example, most wood is less dense than water, so it floats. An object that is more dense than the water it displaces—such as a ship's anchor—will sink.

AIR AND WATER RESISTANCE
When objects travel through the air or water, they are slowed down by the tiny particles of gas or liquid. A thrown ball strikes air particles, which slow it down. In a similar way, swimmers are slowed down by water particles.

AIR PRESSURE
The air is always pushing against things. This is called air pressure. You can increase air pressure by pumping air into a closed space.

MACHINES are devices that make it easier (so less energy is needed) to move an object.

INCLINED PLANE
This is a flat surface with one end higher than the other. It allows heavy objects to be slid up to a higher point rather than be lifted.

WHEEL AND AXLE
This is a wheel with a rod attached to the middle, to help lift loads. The bigger the wheel, the more you have to turn it, but the less effort it takes.

PULLEY
This is made up of a wheel with a groove in it and a rope that fits into the groove. One end of the rope is attached to the load, and you pull the other.

LEVER
This long tool can help to lift or move an object. A long but relatively weak movement at one end can produce a small but forceful movement at the other end.

WEDGE
This has two surfaces at an angle to each other. It can be used to separate two objects, to keep things together, or to prevent movement.

Mike lights the fire, and soon it is burning nicely. Water starts to drip from the ice block. "When all that ice melts, it will create a lot of water," Tess points out.

"A little guy like me might drown," gasps Mike.

"We should try to find something to float on," says Molly.

I've got a sinking feeling.

What objects can they use to help them float when the water level rises?

The ice melts, and the water rises. The four of them cling to their floating objects. Eventually, the water washes into a drain in the floor, and the water level begins to drop. The reversium is now revealed in all its glory ...

It's amazing!

How will we get it out of here?

Outside the lab, they can hear Dr. Smasher shouting. He sounds furious!

"No pressure ... but he's here!" says Andy. "And we're trapped."

"We can escape through there," says Mike, pointing to a locked pair of doors, "if we can get the key out of this." He shows them a corked bottle.

Look, a pump! Do we need more or less pressure in the bottle?

Can you answer Tess's question?

They manage to get the key out of the bottle and open the doors. Parked in the tunnel beyond is a pickup truck.

"We can put the reversium on the back of the truck," says Mike.

"But how can we lift it on?" asks Andy.

"We could create a pulley," says Molly. "We can use one of the bike's wheels and the rope."

All pulley together!

It's still too heavy.

However hard they pull, they cannot lift the reversium. "Maybe we should add another machine to this one?" suggests Andy, eyeing the remaining bicycle wheel and the wooden pole.

What machine can they add to the pulley to help them lift the reversium?

The gang manages to lift the reversium onto the back of the pickup truck. They also take some equipment that might be useful. As they are packing the last of this, Dr. Smasher arrives with his guards.

Seize them!

Molly, Andy, Tess, and Mike make their escape. The tunnel spirals upward through the mountain. Eventually, they emerge on a rocky slope high above the sea. Molly, Andy, and Tess get out to check everything is safe in the back. The slope is very steep, and the truck starts rolling slowly down it toward the edge of a cliff.

The brakes aren't working!

Oh no!

What have they brought with them that could stop the truck rolling?

How can we save him?

Just in time, they stop the truck, and Mike climbs out. However, the reversium and most of their equipment roll off the back! They watch in despair as the precious cargo plunges over the cliff and crashes onto the beach far below.

"We still have some equipment," says Andy, pointing to the rope and canvas sheets.

"We could use the canvas and rope to make a parachute," says Tess. "When we jump off the cliff with it, the parachute will create air resistance. It'll trap lots of air particles, slowing us down."

TESS AND MIKE'S PARACHUTE

MOLLY AND ANDY'S PARACHUTE

Which design of parachute do you think will work better?

The friends choose the right parachute, which takes them down slowly onto the beach. "Look!" Andy points out. "We can escape the island in that submarine."

"But how do we get there with the reversium?" asks Molly.

"We can use that boat," says Tess.

But the reversium is too heavy for them to lift into the boat. They look at the objects scattered on the beach. Is there anything that can help them get the reversium into the boat?

Which of these objects could help them move a heavy object to a higher point?

They manage to get the reversium into the boat. But then they discover the boat has no oars! "Maybe we can use the wooden poles as oars," says Andy. They try using the poles, but they don't work very well.

This is oar-ful!

How are we supposed to row it?

"The poles don't cause much water resistance," says Tess.

"What do you mean?" asks Mike.

"I mean the water flows around them too easily because of their shape." (The diagram below shows what she's talking about!)

The kids decide they need to change the shape of the poles. Mike produces a penknife with a small saw. What object (shown on page 23) could be joined to the poles to improve their shape?

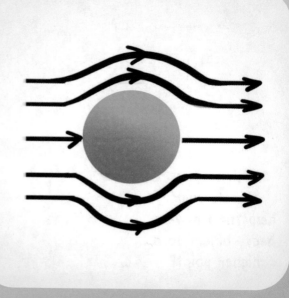

They manage to change the shape of the poles, making them work much better as oars. Soon, they arrive at the submarine and climb aboard. Unfortunately, the hatch is too small for the reversium to fit through it.

They tie the reversium to the sub's tower, then try opening the hatch. However, it becomes stuck. No matter how hard they pull, it won't open.

Eventually, they manage to open the hatch and climb inside the submarine.

"The ballast tank is the part of the submarine that makes it float or sink," says Tess. She checks her screen. "At the moment it's full of air."

Andy remembers their science lesson. "If the density of the submarine is equal to or less than the density of the displaced water, the object will float."

How do we make the submarine go down?

There has to be a way. Let me sink ...

How can they make the submarine sink?

They make the submarine sink, then set a course for home.

Suddenly, the door bursts open. They turn to see Dr. Smasher. "A-ha!" he cackles. "You didn't think it would be that easy to get away, did you? I suspected you would try to steal my submarine, so I stowed myself aboard!"

Now you're in deep water!

"I'm taking you and the reversium back to Atomic Island, where you will stay forever!" declares Dr. Smasher. He pulls a remote control from his pocket and uses it to turn the submarine.

"What now?" Andy groans to Molly. "Listen," she whispers. Andy hears the sounds of helicopters and police sirens, from far above them.

"They'll never catch me down here!" says Smasher. He walks over to the intercom. "Guards, come and tie up these interfering kids." Quick as a flash, Molly presses a button.

What has fast-thinking Molly done? What happens next?

When the submarine reaches the calm surface of the sea, Dr. Smasher realizes that the game is up. "Not the police! I have to get to the reversium. I'll use it to turn them all into babies!" He tries to rush out of the room, but bangs his head on the door, and knocks himself out.

A few days later, the four friends meet at the science museum, where Mike shows them the reversium, back in its case. "I can't thank you enough!" he says. "I'm so glad you saved our best exhibit from being smashed. And I'll soon be back to my old self … no pun intended!"

"I doubt it could have been smashed anyway," says Molly. "It survived being packed in ice, falling off a cliff, and a journey under the sea. I think it might be unbreakable!"

"Just like our friendship!" smiles Tess.

ANSWERS

PAGE 6

Molly should choose to write a message on the base of the copper saucepan, because copper is a soft metal. A plastic bottle is a difficult shape to write on. Steel is too hard. A message in beach sand would wash away.

PAGE 7

Tungsten may be a hard metal, but it is also brittle, so it could easily shatter. Of the other objects available, the steel rod would be the best one to use to break down the door. It is the right shape, and steel is hard.

PAGE 8

Cloth would be a good material to use as a mask because it is permeable. This means it allows air in, so they can breathe. However, it is not too permeable, so it keeps out the most damaging fumes. Silver foil, on the other hand, is not permeable. The tungsten bowl is no use at all, since it won't even cover their mouths properly!

PAGE 9

They should use the tungsten bowl to transport the lava. Tungsten has the highest melting point of any metal. It melts at 3,422 °C (6,192 °F). This is much higher than the temperature of lava, which is 700-1,200 °C (1,292-2,192 °F).

PAGE 10

Metal is a good conductor of heat, so Molly definitely needs to put something between the tungsten bowl and her skin before carrying it. Of the materials they have with them, styrofoam would be the best insulator.

PAGE 11

They can make fresh water from the saltwater lagoon by DISTILLATION. This and the other words you needed to find are highlighted below:

X	U	O	E	O	G	X	G	D	N	R	A
A	A	P	A	L	L	U	R	I	U	M	S
R	P	S	S	R	R	N	G	S	K	S	K
G	A	D	T	E	X	I	O	T	G	E	E
P	S	P	U	T	P	P	S	I	A	G	O
O	E	R	E	A	D	A	X	L	D	C	O
A	R	E	D	W	R	S	R	L	E	X	R
G	P	G	A	T	E	E	E	A	Z	E	R
E	O	G	N	L	D	D	I	T	T	O	E
G	G	L	I	A	E	D	R	I	R	E	P
E	R	S	G	S	O	O	R	O	E	R	S
S	E	O	L	A	G	O	O	N	O	E	A

29

PAGE 12

The answer to the anagram is EVAPORATION. They should pour some saltwater into a bowl and use heat to turn the water into steam. This will leave a residue of salt in the bowl.

PAGE 13

No, concrete cannot be turned back into cement and water. Making concrete is an irreversible change.

PAGE 14

If they heat the ice, it will melt, not burn. Only materials containing carbon burn. When it heats up, the ice will turn into water. If they continue to heat the water, it will turn into steam.

PAGE 15

The materials in the picture that will burn are the ones containing the element carbon. They are the vegetables, the wool, the wood, the leaves, and the coal.

PAGE 18

The objects they can use to help them float when the water rises are the barrel and the two wooden poles.

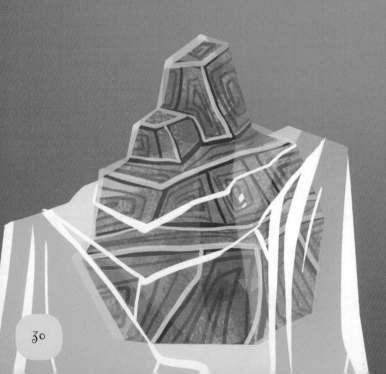

PAGE 19

Tess needs more pressure. Her idea is to insert the nozzle of the bicycle pump through the cork and into the bottle. By pumping air into the bottle it will increase the air pressure inside the bottle so that the cork flies out.

PAGE 20

They could add a wheel and axle machine to the pulley. If they wound the rope around the wooden pole and then attached this to the remaining bicycle wheel, they could then turn the wheel to lift the reversium.

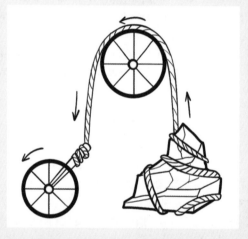

PAGE 21

They could use the two wedges. By placing one of the wedges behind each of the truck's back wheels, it would stop the truck from falling over the cliff.

PAGE 22

Molly and Andy's parachute will work better because it has a larger surface area and a curved interior. This will help it trap more air molecules, creating greater air resistance and giving them a slower, gentler descent to the beach below.

PAGE 23

They could use the wooden plank as an inclined plane. The reversium is too heavy to lift into the boat so they can slide it up the plank instead.

PAGE 24

A good shape for the poles would be broad and flat at the bottom, where they move through the water. If they are broad and flat, this will create more water resistance, pushing the boat forward. They can use the wooden plank to improve the shape of the poles. The plank could be cut into two halves, and each half could be tied to the end of each of the poles with rope.

PAGE 25

They can use the steel rod as a lever to force open the hatch.

PAGE 26

They should fill the submarine's ballast tank with water. This will make the submarine denser overall than the water it has displaced, so it will sink.

PAGE 27

What goes down, must come up! Molly presses a button that fills the submarine's ballast tank with air. Air is less dense than the water it displaces, and so will make the submarine rise to the surface. Once they reach the surface, the police will spot Dr. Smasher, and arrest him!

GLOSSARY

AIR RESISTANCE A type of friction between air and another object, making it harder for the object to move.

BALLAST TANK A compartment in a boat that holds water, used to provide stability.

CONCRETE A material used for building, which is made by mixing cement, sand, small stones, and water.

CONDUCTOR A material that heat or electricity can pass through or along.

CURATOR A person in charge of objects in a museum.

DENSITY The relation of an object's mass or weight to its volume.

DISPLACED Moved from its usual position.

EXTRACT To take or pull out.

INSULATOR A material that does not conduct heat or electricity well.

LAVA Very hot, liquid rock that comes out of a volcano.

LOCOMOTIVE A large vehicle that pulls a railway train.

MELTING POINT The temperature at which a substance melts when heated.

PROPERTIES Distinctive features of a material.

PULLEY A device used to lift heavy objects, made from a rope or chain pulled over a wheel.

STYROFOAM A light, polystyrene plastic.

TUNGSTEN A greyish-white metal.

WATER RESISTANCE A type of friction between water and an object, making it harder for the object to move.

FURTHER INFORMATION

DK Publishing. *Knowledge Encyclopedia Science!* London, UK. DK Children, 2018

O'Briain, Dara. *Secret Science: The Amazing World Beyond Your Eyes.* London, UK. Scholastic, 2018

INDEX